IF...

GOES
DOWN
THE
JOHN

D0248793

Steve Bell

IF...

GOES
DOWN
THE
JOHN

MANDARIN

For Heather, William, Joey, Paddy and Kit Kat

This collection first published in Great Britain in 1992
by Mandarin Paperbacks
Michelin House, 81 Fulham Road, London SW3 6RB

Mandarin is an imprint of the Octopus Publishing Group,
a division of Reed International Books Ltd

The strips first published by the *Guardian* in 1991 and 1992

Copyright © Steve Bell 1991, 1992
The author has asserted his moral rights

Designed by Brian Homer
Production by Andy Coyne
Edited by Steve Bell and Brian Homer

Linotronic playout by Typesetters, Birmingham Ltd

Printed and bound in Great Britain
by Clays Ltd, St Ives plc

A CIP catalogue record for this book
is available from the British Library
ISBN 0 7493 1144 4

7

8

9

10

14

15

16

17

18

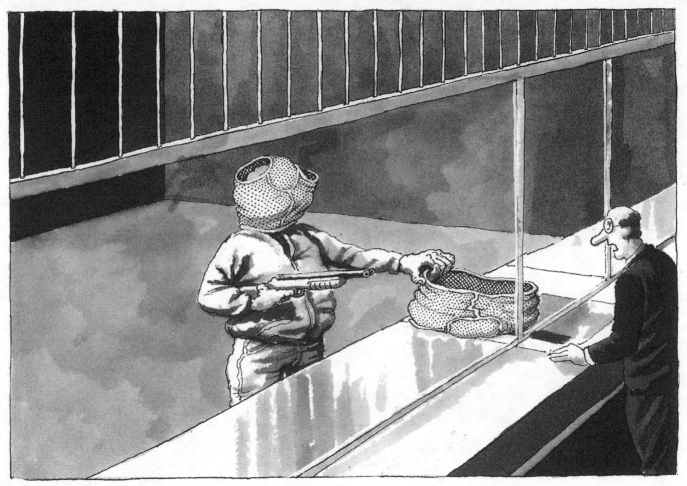

23

24

25

27

28

29

31

35

36

38

39

42

43

44

47

48

49

50

53

55

56

HOW DO WE PLAY "LABOUR WOG-SCARE" KEN??
FIRST WE TURN OUT ALL THE LIGHTS!
11-10-2773
THEN WE TELL SCARE STORIES, LIKE THIS:...
HEE HEE!
OOOO!
©Steve Bell 1991
"WITH LABOUR'S HELP, MILLIONS OF MAD GREEDY WOGS ARE PLOTTING TO ENTER BRITAIN BY POSING AS POLITICAL ASYLUM SEEKERS!"
HOOOO HOOOOO WOOOO WOOOO!
HOOOOO WOOOOO!
HOOO HOOOO!! "LABOUR WOG-SCARE" IS FUN!!
EEEEEK!
HELLLLOO!
WHO'S THAT??
I KNOW A VERY SCAREY GAME: IT'S CALLLLED TWO MILLLLION BILLLLION EXTRA UNEMPLLLLOYED PEEPILLLL UNDER LLLABOUR!
IS THAT YOU, HOWARD?
HOW DO WE PLAY THIS GAME??
WE CLLLOSE OUR EYES AND SAY: TWO MILLLLION BILLLLION TRILLLLION UNEMPLLLOYED PEEPILLLL SHOULD LLLLABOUR EVER GET IN!!
THAT'S STRETCHING IT A BIT, HOWARD - WHY DO YOU KEEP CHANGING THE FIGURES??
BECAUSE I'M AN IMPLLLAUSIBULLLL PILLLLOCK!!
©Steve Bell 1991-

60

61

64

65

68

71

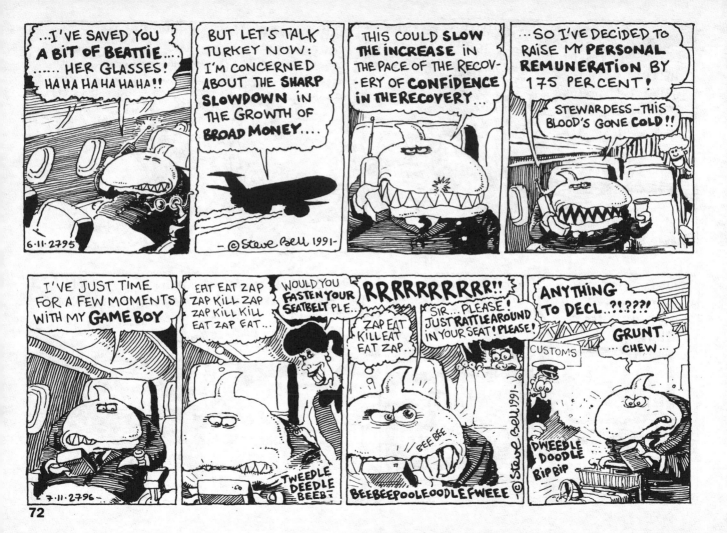

72

74

80

87

88

89

90

91

92

UNEMPLOYMENT UP, INFLATION UP....
-23-12-2835-
...THE ACCELERATION OF THE SLOWDOWN IN THE DOWNWARD GROWTH OF BROAD MONEY HAS INTENS--IFIED......
© Steve Bell 1991
...AND NOW THE KRAUTS HAVE PUT UP THEIR INTEREST RATES!..
I THINK I'LL TURN INTO A BAT!

24·12·2836
House of Discipline
WOULD SIR LIKE SOMETHING FOR THE WEEKEND?
I WANT A STOUT LASH AND SOME RUBBER CHAINS!
CERTAINLY SIR
DOES SIR WANT THEM WRAPPED?
NO NEED, THANKYOU!
COME ON SCUM! ONLY ONE SHOPPING DAY TO XMAS! SPEND!! RECOVER!! YOU DOGS!!
CRACK
LASH
FLAIL
FLAIL
© Steve Bell '91

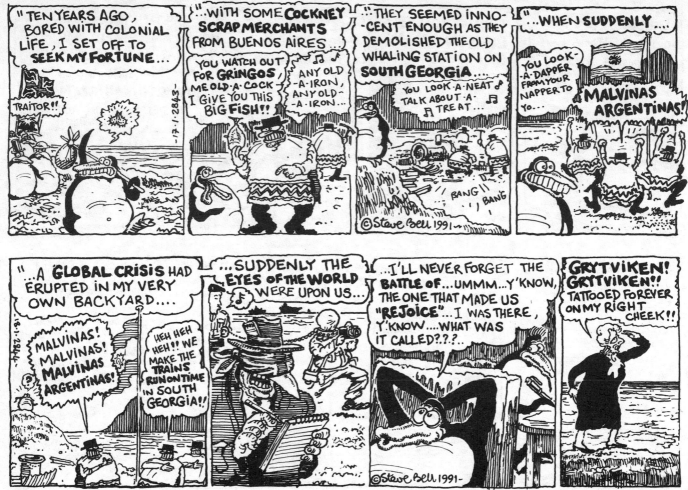

100

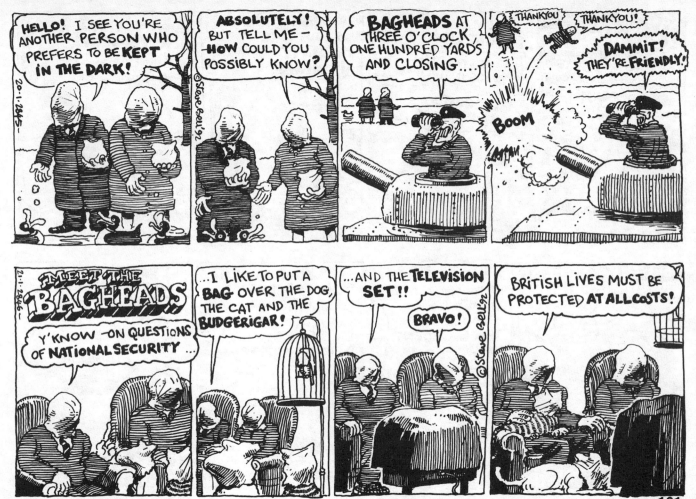

103

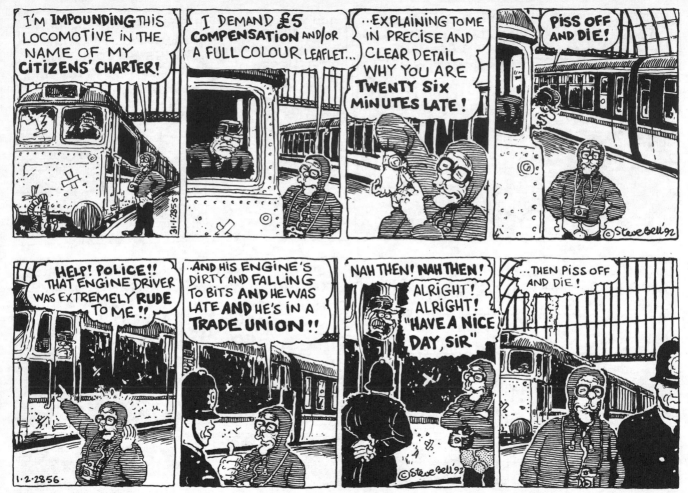

106

108

109

112

113

115

120

123

124

125

126

127

128

129

133

137

140

143

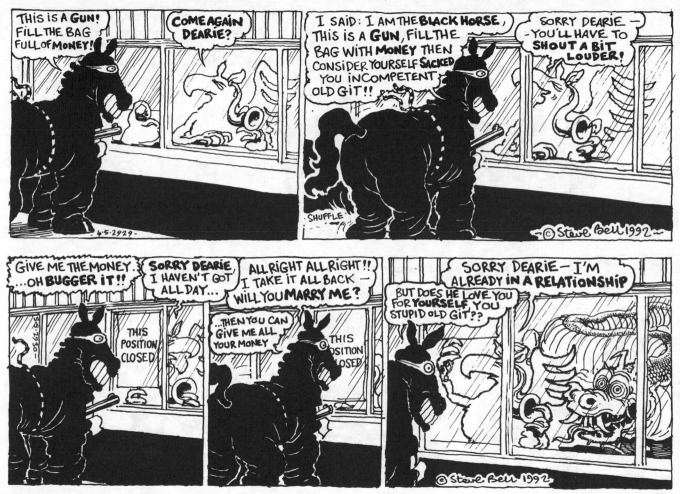

151

152

153

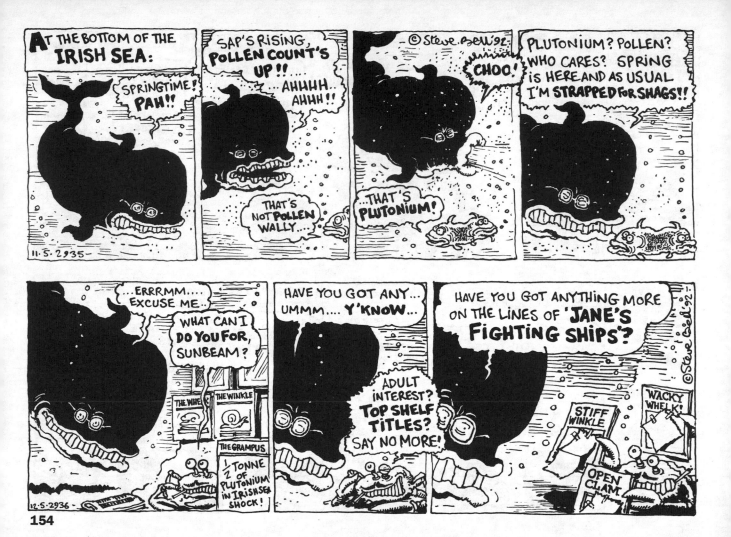

154

155

157

158

159

©Steve Bell 1992 —

AFTER GAINSBOROUGH   143-21-5-92